Swing!
HERE AND NOW

The Music of Harry Warren

Arranged by GEORGE ROUMANIS

CONDUCTOR BOOK includes the
CD Recording of the *George Roumanis Big Band*
ROCKSMITH RECORDINGS (RM0002)

CDs available from:
ROCKSMITH RECORDINGS, LLC
P.O. BOX 22274
CARMEL, CA 93922

CONTE

INSTRUMENTATION

Conductor—SBM00013CD
1st E♭ Alto Saxophone—SBM00014
2nd E♭ Alto Saxophone—SBM00015
1st B♭ Tenor Saxophone—SBM00016
2nd B♭ Tenor Saxophone—SBM00017
E♭ Baritone Saxophone—SBM00018
1st B♭ Trumpet—SBM00019
2nd B♭ Trumpet—SBM00020
3rd B♭ Trumpet—SBM00021
4th B♭ Trumpet—SBM00022
1st Trombone—SBM00023
2nd Trombone—SBM00024
3rd Trombone—SBM00025
4th Trombone—SBM00026
Piano—SBM00027
Guitar—SBM00028
Bass—SBM00029
Drums—SBM00030

CONDUCTOR
SBM00013CD

CHATTANOOGA CHOO CHOO

Words by MACK GORDON
Music by HARRY WARREN
Arranged by GEORGE ROUMANIS

7
Alto 1
Alto 2
Tenor 1
Tenor 2
Bari.
Push
1.
Tpt. 1
Tpt. 2
Tpt. 3
Tpt. 4
Plunger
Tbn. 1
Tbn. 2
Tbn. 3
Tbn. 4
Gtr.
Pno.
Bass
Drums
C6
B6
Dmi7
Dmi7/G
B6/9
C6/9
(Saxes)
7
8
9
10
11
12
13
14

2.
17
Play All Times
Tacet on D.S. for Bass Solo
Alto 1
Alto 2
Tenor 1
Tenor 2
Bari.
Tpt. 1
Tpt. 2
Tpt. 3
Tpt. 4
Tbn. 1
Tbn. 2
Tbn. 3
Tbn. 4
Gtr.
Pno.
Bass
Drums
mf
cresc.
Open
C6 B6 C6
FMaj7 C7(#9) FMaj7 C7(#9) FMaj7 C7(#9) FMaj7 Cmi7/F
B♭ Bmi7 E7 F E♭7 D7 G7(♭9)
B♭6/9 C6/9
Bass Solo on D.S.
Solo on D.S.
Tpts.
Brass
15
16
17
18
19
20
21
22
23

1.)
2.)
PLAY ALL TIMES
28
ALTO 1
ALTO 2
TENOR 1
TENOR 2
BARI.
TPT. 1
TPT. 2
TPT. 3
TPT. 4
TBN. 1
TBN. 2
TBN. 3
TBN. 4
GTR.
PNO.
BASS
DRUMS
C7(#9)
G7(#9)
C7
F
DMI7/G
A♭MA7
G7
C6
B6
B6/9
C6/9
ENS.
24
25
26
27
28
29
30
31

32
Alto 1
Alto 2
Tenor 1
Tenor 2
Bari.
Tpt. 1
Play 1st Time Only
Tpt. 2
Solo - on D.S. only
Tpt. 3
Tpt. 4
Push
Solo - 1st Time Only
Tbn. 1
Play on D.S.
Tbn. 2
Tbn. 3
Tbn. 4
Gtr.
C6
B6
Dmi7
Dmi7/G
Pno.
Bass
Drums
(Tpts.)
32
33
34
35
36
37
38

Alto 1
Alto 2
Tenor 1
Tenor 2
Bari.
Tpt. 1
Tpt. 2
Tpt. 3
Tpt. 4
Tbn. 1
Tbn. 2
Tbn. 3
Tbn. 4
Gtr.
Pno.
Bass
Drums
8va
C6
B6
F
A♭9
D7
Cmaj7
Ami7
A♭7
G7
B6♭9
C6♭9
Ens.
39
40
41
42
43
44
45

TO CODA
ALTO 1
ALTO 2
TENOR 1
SOLO
TENOR 2
BARI.
TPT. 1
TPT. 2
TPT. 3
TPT. 4
TBN. 1
TBN. 2
TBN. 3
TBN. 4
GTR.
C C7 F7 F#DIM G7 C C7 F7 F#DIM G7 C C7 F7 F#DIM DMI7 CMAJ7
PNO.
BASS
TPTS.
DRUMS
46
47
48
49
50
51
52
53

54
Alto 1
Alto 2
Tenor 1
Tenor 2
Bari.
Tpt. 1
Tpt. 2
Tpt. 3
Tpt. 4
Tbn. 1
Tbn. 2
Tbn. 3
Tbn. 4
Gtr.
Pno.
Bass
Drums
mf
Gmaj7 G#dim Dmaj7/A D7 Gmaj7 G#dim Dmaj7/A D7 Gmaj7 G#dim Dmaj7 B7 E9 A9 D9
End Solo
Fmaj7 F#dim Cmaj7/G C7 Fmaj7 F#dim Cmaj7/G C7 Fmaj7 F#dim Cmaj7 A7 D9 G9 C9
(Sax Solo)
54 55 56 57 58 59 60 61

62
D.S. % AL CODA (WITH REPEAT)
ALTO 1
ALTO 2
TENOR 1
TENOR 2
BARI.
TPT. 1
TPT. 2
TPT. 3
TPT. 4
TBN. 1
TBN. 2
TBN. 3
TBN. 4
GTR.
FMAJ7 F#DIM CMAJ7/G C7 FMAJ7 F#DIM CMAJ7/G C7 FMAJ7 F#DIM CMAJ7 A7 D7 G7 C7
PNO.
SOLO - AD LIB.
FMAJ7 F#DIM CMAJ7/G C7 FMAJ7 F#DIM CMAJ7/G C7 FMAJ7 F#DIM CMAJ7 A7 D7 G7 C7
END SOLO
BASS
DRUMS
(PIANO SOLO)
TPTS.
mf
62 63 64 65 66 67 68 69

Coda
Alto 1
Alto 2
Tenor 1
Tenor 2
Bari.
Tpt. 1
Tpt. 2
Tpt. 3
Tpt. 4
Tbn. 1
Tbn. 2
Tbn. 3
Tbn. 4
Gtr.
Pno.
Bass
Drums
F7
F♯dim
Dmi7
Cmaj7
70
71
72
73

I HAD THE CRAZIEST DREAM

Words by MACK GORDON
Music by HARRY WARREN
Arranged by GEORGE ROUMANIS

9
Alto 1
Alto 2
Tenor 1
Tenor 2
Bari.
Tpt. 1
Tpt. 2
Tpt. 3
Solo - Sing
Tpt. 4
Tbn. 1
Tbn. 2
Tbn. 3
Tbn. 4
Gtr.
Pno.
Bass
(Tpt. Solo)
Drums
E♭6 Gm7(♭5) C7(♭9) C+7 Fm7 C7(♭9) Fm7 C7(♭9) Fm7 Fm7/B♭ Fm7 B♭7 E♭6 G♭dim Fm7 B♭7
9 10 11 12 13 14 15 16

Alto 1
Alto 2
Tenor 1
Tenor 2
Bari.
Tpt. 1
Tpt. 2
Tpt. 3
Tpt. 4
Tbn. 1
Tbn. 2
Tbn. 3
Tbn. 4
Gtr.
Pno.
Bass
Drums
Gm7(b5) C7(b9) Gm7(b5) C7(b9) Fm7 Gm7(b5) C7(b9) Fm Am7(b5) D7(b9) Am7(b5) D7(b9) Gm7 G♭dim
17
18
19
20
21
22
23

Alto 1
Alto 2
Tenor 1
Tenor 2
Bari.
Tpt. 1
Tpt. 2
Tpt. 3
Tpt. 4
Tbn. 1
Tbn. 2
Tbn. 3
Tbn. 4
Gtr.
Pno.
Bass
Drums
Ens.
24
25
26
27
28
29
30
31

32
36
Alto 1
Alto 2
Tenor 1
Tenor 2
Bari.
Tpt. 1
Tpt. 2
Tpt. 3
Tpt. 4
Tbn. 1
Tbn. 2
Tbn. 3
Tbn. 4
Gtr.
Pno.
Bass
Drums
mf
SIM.
Fm7 Gm7 Fm7
G♭m7 B9
Fm7 Gm7 Fm7
D♭m7 G♭7
F
Am7(♭5) D7 D+7
Gm7 D7(♭9)
Gm7 D+7
Drive - Ens.
32
33
34
35
36
37
38
39

Alto 1
Alto 2
Tenor 1
Tenor 2
Bari.
Tpt. 1
Tpt. 2
Tpt. 3
Tpt. 4
Tbn. 1
Tbn. 2
Tbn. 3
Tbn. 4
Gtr.
Pno.
Bass
Drums
Gm7 C7 C+7 F A♭dim Gm7 C7 Am7(♭5) D7(♭9) Am7(♭5) D7(♭9) Gm6 Cm6 D7(♭9) Gm6
40 41 42 43 44 45 46 47

Alto 1
Alto 2
Tenor 1
Tenor 2
Bari.
Tpt. 1
Tpt. 2
Tpt. 3
Tpt. 4
Tbn. 1
Tbn. 2
Tbn. 3
Tbn. 4
Gtr.
Pno.
Bass
Drums
Bm7(b5) E7 Bm7(b5) E7 Am7 A♭dim Gm7 C7 F Am7(b5) D7 D+7 Gm7 D7(b9)
48 49 50 51 52 53 54

Alto 1
Alto 2
Tenor 1
Tenor 2
Bari.
Tpt. 1
Tpt. 2
Tpt. 3
Tpt. 4
Solo ad lib. (Harmon or plunger)
G7
C7
(2 bar break)
Tbn. 1
Tbn. 2
Tbn. 3
Tbn. 4
Gtr.
Pno.
Bass
Drums
Gm7
E♭9
F
A7
Dm7
G7
Gm7
F13
(Tpt. Solo Break)
55
56
57
58
59
60
61

62
Alto 1
Alto 2
Tenor 1
Tenor 2
Bari.
Tpt. 1
Tpt. 2
Tpt. 3
Tpt. 4
Tbn. 1
Tbn. 2
Tbn. 3
Tbn. 4
Gtr.
Pno.
Bass
Drums
mf
(Tpt. Solo)
F Am7(b5) D7(b9) Gm7 D7(b9) Gm7 D7(b9) Gm7 C9 Fmaj7 D7(b9) Gm7 C7(b9)
Eb Gm7(b5) C7(b9) Fm7 C7(b9) Fm7 C7(b9) Fm7 Bb9 Ebmaj7 C7(b9) Fm7 Bb7(b9)
62 63 64 65 66 67 68 69

Alto 1
Alto 2
Tenor 1
Tenor 2
Bari.
Tpt. 1
Tpt. 2
Tpt. 3
Tpt. 4
Am7(b5) D7(#9) Gm6 Am7(b5) D7(b9) Gm Bm7(b5) E7 Am7 A♭dim Gm7 C+7
Tbn. 1
Tbn. 2
Tbn. 3
Tbn. 4
Gtr.
Pno.
Bass
Gm7(b5) C7(#9) Fm6 Gm7(b5) C7(b9) Fm Am7(b5) D7 Gm7 G♭dim Fm7 B♭+7
Drums
70
71
72
73
74
75
76
77

78
Alto 1
Alto 2
Tenor 1
Tenor 2
Bari.
Tpt. 1
Tpt. 2
Tpt. 3
Tpt. 4
Tbn. 1
Tbn. 2
Tbn. 3
Tbn. 4
Gtr.
Pno.
Bass
Drums
E♭maj7
Gm7(♭5)
C+7(♭9)
A♭6
C7(♭9)
Fm7
D♭9
E♭maj7
G7
Cm7
F7
Fm7
B♭7
Gm7(♭5)
D♭9
C9
C7(♯9)
Ens.
(Tpt. Solo)
78
79
80
81
82
83
84
85

Alto 1
Alto 2
Tenor 1
Tenor 2
Bari.
Tpt. 1
Tpt. 2
Tpt. 3
Tpt. 4
Tbn. 1
Tbn. 2
Tbn. 3
Tbn. 4
Gtr.
E♭maj7
Pno.
8vb
Bass
Drums
Fill
86
87
88
89

FORTY SECOND STREET

Words by AL DUBIN
Music by HARRY WARREN
Arranged by GEORGE ROUMANIS

Alto 1
Alto 2
Tenor 1
Tenor 2
Bari.
Tpt. 1
Tpt. 2
Tpt. 3
Tpt. 4
Tbn. 1
Tbn. 2
Tbn. 3
Tbn. 4
Gtr.
Pno.
Bass
Drums
11
(Alto Sax)
Play 2nd Time Only
(Plunger)
(Plunger)
Gm6 Eb9 Gm6 C9 Eb9 D+7 Gm6 Am6 Gm6 Eb9 D9 Gm6 Gm7 Cm7 F7
Gm6 Eb9 Gm6 C9 Eb9 D+7 Gm6 Am6 Gm6 Eb9 D9 Gm6 Gm7 Cm7 F7
Solo around melody
9
10
11
12
13
14
15

1.)
2.)
ALTO 1
ALTO 2
TENOR 1
TENOR 2
BARI.
TPT. 1
TPT. 2
TPT. 3
TPT. 4
TBN. 1
TBN. 2
TBN. 3
TBN. 4
GTR.
PNO.
BASS
DRUMS
Gm7 Am7 B♭m7 E♭9 Am7 A♭9 Gm6
Gm6 C9 E♭9 D9 Gm6
FILL
SOLO
16
17
18
19
20
21
22

23
Alto 1
Alto 2
Tenor 1
Tenor 2
Bari.
Tpt. 1
Tpt. 2
Tpt. 3
Tpt. 4
Tbn. 1
Tbn. 2
Tbn. 3
Tbn. 4
Gtr.
Pno.
Bass
Drums
E♭7
C9
A♭M7 D♭7 AM7 D9
23 24 25 26 27 28 29 30

31
ALTO 1
ALTO 2
TENOR 1
TENOR 2
BARI.
TPT. 1
TPT. 2
TPT. 3
TPT. 4
TBN. 1
TBN. 2
TBN. 3
TBN. 4
GTR.
PNO.
BASS
DRUMS
OPEN
OPEN
Gm6 Eb9 Gm6 C9 Eb9 D+7 Gm6 Am6 Gm6 Eb9 D9 Gm6 Gm7 Cm7 F7 Gm7 Am7 Bbm7 Eb9 Am7 Ab9 Gm6 Eb7(#9) D7(#9)
TO STICKS
(STICKS)
FILL
31 32 33 34 35 36 37 38

39
Alto 1
Alto 2
Tenor 1
Tenor 2
Bari.
Tpt. 1
Tpt. 2
Tpt. 3
Tpt. 4
Tbn. 1
Tbn. 2
Tbn. 3
Tbn. 4
Gtr.
Pno.
Bass
Drums
Rip
(Solo - ad lib.)
(Piano Solo - 8 bars)
End Solo
E♭9
C9
A♭M7
D♭9
Am7
D9
39
40
41
42
43
44
45
46

47
(SOLI)
ALTO 1
ALTO 2
TENOR 1
TENOR 2
BARI.
TPT. 1
TPT. 2
TPT. 3
TPT. 4
TBN. 1
TBN. 2
TBN. 3
TBN. 4
mf
GTR.
PNO.
BASS
DRUMS
(SAX SOLI)
Gm6 C9 Eb9 D7 Gm6 Am7(b5) Gm6 D7 Gm6 Cm7 F7 Gm7 Abm7 Am7 Bbm7 Eb7 Gm6 Gm(maj7) Gm7 Gm6
47
48
49
50
51
52
53
54

57
Alto 1
Alto 2
Tenor 1
Tenor 2
Bari.
Tpt. 1
Tpt. 2
Tpt. 3
Tpt. 4
Tbn. 1
Tbn. 2
Tbn. 3
Tbn. 4
Gtr.
Pno.
Bass
Drums
Am7 A♭9 Gm6 E♭7(♯9) D7(♯9) N.C.
Am7 A♭9 Gm6 E♭7(♯9) D7(♯9) N.C.
Solo
55
56
57
58
59
60
61
62

Alto 1
Alto 2
Tenor 1
Tenor 2
Bari.
Tpt. 1
Tpt. 2
Tpt. 3
Tpt. 4
Tbn. 1
Tbn. 2
Tbn. 3
Tbn. 4
Gtr.
Pno.
Bass
Drums
(SOLO)
63
64
65
66
67
68
69

Alto 1
Alto 2
Tenor 1
Tenor 2
Bari.
Tpt. 1
Tpt. 2
Tpt. 3
Tpt. 4
Tbn. 1
Tbn. 2
Tbn. 3
Tbn. 4
Gtr.
Pno.
Bass
Drums
To Clarinet
Solo
70
71
72
73
74
75
76

77 Play 4x's
Clarinet
83
Alto 1
Alto 2
Tenor 1
Tenor 2
Bari.
Plunger
Play Last Time Only
St. Mute
Tpt. 1
Play Last Time Only
Tpt. 2
Play 3rd+4th Times Only
Tpt. 3
Play 3rd+4th Times Only
Tpt. 4
Plunger
Tacet 1st Time
Open
Tbn. 1
Tbn. 2
Tbn. 3
Tbn. 4
Gm6
Gtr.
Pno.
Bass
Solo
Drums
77
78
79
80
81
82
83
84

Alto 1
Alto 2
Tenor 1
Tenor 2
Bari.
(To Alto Sax)
Tpt. 1
Tpt. 2
Tpt. 3
Tpt. 4
(Plunger)
Tbn. 1
Tbn. 2
Tbn. 3
Tbn. 4
(Plunger)
Gtr.
Pno.
Bass
Drums
(Solo)
(Solo)
85
86
87
88
89
90
91
92

Alto Sax
99 Play 3x's
Alto 1
Alto 2
Tenor 1
Tenor 2
Bari.
Tpt. 1
Tpt. 2
Tpt. 3
Tpt. 4
Lead Open
Open
Tbn. 1
Tbn. 2
Tbn. 3
Tbn. 4
Gtr.
Pno.
Bass
Drums
Gm6 Eb9 Gm6 C9 Eb9 D+7 Gm6 Am6 Gm6 Eb9 D9 Gm6 Gm7 Cm7 F7 Gm7 Am7 Bbm7 Eb9 Gm7 EbM6/Gb Bb/F Em7(b5) EbMA7
93
94
95
96
97
98
99
100

1., 2.)
3.)
ALTO 1
ALTO 2
TENOR 1
TENOR 2
BARI.
TPT. 1
TPT. 2
TPT. 3
TPT. 4
TBN. 1
TBN. 2
TBN. 3
TBN. 4
GTR.
PNO.
BASS
DRUMS
OPEN
OPEN
PLUNGER
PLUNGER
N.C.
Gm6
E♭9
D9
N.C.
N.C.
Gm6
E♭9
D9
N.C.
SOLO
SOLO
101
102
103
104
105
106
107
108

THE MORE I SEE YOU

Words by MACK GORDON
Music by HARRY WARREN
Arranged by GEORGE ROUMANIS

SOLI - VIB.
ALTO 1
ALTO 2
TENOR 1
TENOR 2
BARI.
TPT. 1
TPT. 2
TPT. 3
TPT. 4
TBN. 1
TBN. 2
TBN. 3
TBN. 4
SOLO
GTR.
PNO.
BASS
DRUMS
9
10
11
12
13
14
15
16

21
Alto 1
Alto 2
Tenor 1
Tenor 2
Bari.
Tpt. 1
Tpt. 2
Tpt. 3
Tpt. 4
Tbn. 1
Tbn. 2
Tbn. 3
Tbn. 4
Gtr.
Pno.
Bass
Drums
17
18
19
20
21
22
23
24
25

Alto 1
Alto 2
Tenor 1
Tenor 2
Bari.
Tpt. 1
Tpt. 2
Tpt. 3
Tpt. 4
Tbn. 1
Tbn. 2
Tbn. 3
Tbn. 4
Gtr.
Pno.
Bass
Drums
Cm7 A+7 E♭M7 Fm7 G♭maj7 Gm7(♭5) A♭9 A9 E♭M7 D9 D♭maj7 G9 D♭M7/G♭ G♭9 B♭m7(♭5) E♭7 A♭maj7 B♭m7 A♭6/C Fm7 Fm7/E♭ Dm7(♭5) D♭m6 Cm7 F7(♭9)
mf
ml
Ens.
26
27
28
29
30
31
32
33

37
Alto 1
Alto 2
Tenor 1
Solo - Ad Lib.
Tenor 2
Bari.
Tpt. 1
Tpt. 2
Tpt. 3
Tpt. 4
Tbn. 1
Tbn. 2
Tbn. 3
Tbn. 4
Gtr.
Pno.
Bass
Tenor Solo
Drums
34
35
36
37
38
39
40
41
42

ALTO 1
ALTO 2
TENOR 1
TENOR 2
BARI.
TPT. 1
TPT. 2
TPT. 3
TPT. 4
TBN. 1
TBN. 2
TBN. 3
TBN. 4
GTR.
PNO.
BASS
DRUMS
Fm9
Bb7 END SOLO
Ebm9
A9
Eb7
D9
Dbmaj7
G9
Dbm7/Gb
Gb9
Bbm7(b5)
Eb7
Abmaj7
Bbm7
Ab6/C
Fm7
Fm7/Eb
Dm7(b5)
Dbm6
Cm7
F7(b9)
Bbm7
Bbm7/Eb
Eb9
43
44
45
46
47
48
49
50

Alto 1
Alto 2
Tenor 1
Tenor 2
Bari.
Tpt. 1
Tpt. 2
Tpt. 3
Tpt. 4
Tbn. 1
Tbn. 2
Tbn. 3
Tbn. 4
Gtr.
Pno.
Bass
Drums
Arco - Slow gliss. on E String
Mallets on Cym.
51
52
53
54
55
56
57
58

LULU'S BACK IN TOWN

Words by AL DUBIN
Music by HARRY WARREN
Arranged by GEORGE ROUMANIS

1.)
2.)
Alto 1
Alto 2
Tenor 1
Tenor 2
Bari.
Play Both Times
Tpt. 1
Tpt. 2
Tpt. 3
Tpt. 4
Tbn. 1
Plunger
Tbn. 2
Tbn. 3
Open
Tbn. 4
Gtr.
Pno.
Bass
Swing
Drums
E♭7 A♭6 Dm7 G7 E♭maj7 C9 F9 B♭7 E♭ G♭9 F9 B♭+7 F9 B♭7 E♭ E♭9
8vb
8
9
10
11
12
13
14

15
ALTO 1
ALTO 2
TENOR 1
TENOR 2
BARI.
TROMBONE LEAD
TPT. 1
TPT. 2
TPT. 3
TPT. 4
WAH
OPEN
UNIS. SOLI
TBN. 1
TBN. 2
TBN. 3
TBN. 4
LEAD
GTR.
PNO.
BASS
DRUMS
A♭MA7 ADIM E♭MA7 E♭9 A♭MA7 ADIM E♭MA7 E♭9 AM7(♭5) D7(♭9) GM7 C+7 F9 B♭9 FM7
(8VB)
15
16
17
18
19
20
21
22

23
Alto 1
Alto 2
Tenor 1
Tenor 2
Bari.
Tpt. 1
Tpt. 2
Tpt. 3
Tpt. 4
Tbn. 1
Tbn. 2
Tbn. 3
Tbn. 4
Gtr.
Pno.
Bass
Drums
mf
Lead
Div.
Fill
A♭maj7 A dim E♭maj7 E♭7(♯9) A♭maj7 A dim E♭maj7 E♭7(♯9) Am7(♭5) D7(♯9) Gm7 C9 C+7(♭9) E9 F9 B9 B♭9
23 24 25 26 27 28 29 30

31
Alto 1
Alto 2
Tenor 1
Tenor 2
Bari.
Tpt. 1
Tpt. 2
Tpt. 3
Tpt. 4
Tbn. 1
Tbn. 2
Tbn. 3
Tbn. 4
Gtr.
Pno.
Bass
Drums
Plunger
Toms
Swing
mf
E♭6 F7 B♭7 E♭6 E♭7 A♭6 Dm7 G7 E♭maj7 C9 F9 B♭7 E♭6 E♭maj7 B♭9
31 32 33 34 35 36 37 38

39
1.)
Alto 1
Alto 2
Tenor 1
Tenor 2
Bari.
Tenor Lead
Lead
Growl
Tpt. 1
Tpt. 2
Tpt. 3
Tpt. 4
Tbn. 1
Tbn. 2
Tbn. 3
Tbn. 4
Gtr.
Pno.
Bass
Drums
Toms
Swing
39
40
41
42
43
44
45
46

2.)
49
TENOR LEAD
LEAD
SOLO 2ND TIME
SOLO 1ST TIME
OPEN
ALTO 1
ALTO 2
TENOR 1
TENOR 2
BARI.
TPT. 1
TPT. 2
TPT. 3
TPT. 4
TBN. 1
TBN. 2
TBN. 3
TBN. 4
GTR.
PNO.
BASS
DRUMS
47
48
49
50
51
52
53
54

1.)
2.)
59
Alto 1
Alto 2
Tenor 1
Tenor 2
Bari.
Tpt. 1
Tpt. 2
Tpt. 3
Tpt. 4
Tbn. 1
Tbn. 2
Tbn. 3
Tbn. 4
Gtr.
Pno.
Bass
Drums
D9
Dm7/G
End Solo
F9
B♭9
E♭9
End Solo
Fm7/B♭
E♭maj7
E♭6
Am7(♭5)
Dm7(♭5)
E♭6
mf
As Is - Soli w/Horns
(Play Hi-Hat, No Bass Drum)
55
56
57
58
59
60
61
62

67
Alto 1
Alto 2
Tenor 1
Tenor 2
Bari.
Tpt. 1
Tpt. 2
Tpt. 3
Tpt. 4
Tbn. 1
Tbn. 2
Tbn. 3
Tbn. 4
Gtr.
Pno.
Bass
Drums
Am7(b5)
Dm7(b5)
Am7(b5)
Dm7(b5)
Eb6
Am7(b5)
Dm7(b5)
Eb6
63
64
65
66
67
68
69
70

Alto 1
Alto 2
Tenor 1
Tenor 2
Bari.
Tpt. 1
Tpt. 2
Tpt. 3
Tpt. 4
Tacet 1st Time
Tbn. 1
Tbn. 2
Tbn. 3
Tbn. 4
Gtr.
Pno.
Bass
Drums
Kick It
75
71
72
73
74
75
76
77
78

1.)
2.)
85
ALTO 1
ALTO 2
TENOR 1
TENOR 2
BARI.
TPT. 1
TPT. 2
TPT. 3
TPT. 4
PLUNGER
TBN. 1
TBN. 2
TBN. 3
TBN. 4
GTR.
PNO.
BASS
DRUMS
SOLO
TOMS
A♭MAJ7 A♭6 ADIM
E♭MAJ7 D7(♯9) D♭7(♯9) C7(♯9)
F9
F9 E9 F9 B9 B♭9
79
80
81
82
83
84
85
86

Alto 1
Alto 2
Tenor 1
Tenor 2
Bari.
Tpt. 1
Tpt. 2
Tpt. 3
Tpt. 4
Tbn. 1
Tbn. 2
Tbn. 3
Tbn. 4
Gtr.
Pno.
Bass
Drums
Open
Plunger
Swing
E♭7 A♭6 Dm7 G7 E♭maj7 C9 F9 B♭9 E♭ D♭9 C9 F9 B♭9
87
88
89
90
91
92
93

ALTO 1
ALTO 2
TENOR 1
TENOR 2
BARI.
TPT. 1
TPT. 2
TPT. 3
TPT. 4
TBN. 1
TBN. 2
TBN. 3
TBN. 4
GTR.
PNO.
BASS
DRUMS
OPTIONAL
PLAY
94
95
96
97
98
99
100

YOU'LL NEVER KNOW

Words by MACK GORDON
Music by HARRY WARREN
Arranged by GEORGE ROUMANIS

Alto 1
Alto 2
Tenor 1
Tenor 2
Bari.
Tpt. 1
Tpt. 2
Tpt. 3
Tpt. 4
Tbn. 1
Tbn. 2
Tbn. 3
Tbn. 4
Gtr.
Pno.
Bass
Drums
Gm7
Gm7/C
F6
Fmaj7
Gm7
D♭m7/G♭
G♭9
Fmaj7
A♭dim
Gm7
D+7
Gm7
E♭9
D7(♯9)
9
10
11
12
13
14
15
16

21
ALTO 1
ALTO 2
TENOR 1
TENOR 2
BARI.
TPT. 1
TPT. 2
TPT. 3
TPT. 4
TBN. 1
TBN. 2
TBN. 3
TBN. 4
GTR.
PNO.
BASS
DRUMS
Gm7 C7 Gm7 C7 Am7 A♭m7 Gm7 C7(♭9) Fmaj7 F(NO3RD) Am7 A♭m7 Gm7 Gm7 A♭dim
17 18 19 20 21 22 23 24

Alto 1
Alto 2
Tenor 1
Tenor 2
Bari.
Tpt. 1
Tpt. 2
Tpt. 3
To Trumpet
Tpt. 4
Tbn. 1
Tbn. 2
Tbn. 3
Tbn. 4
Gtr.
Pno.
Bass
Drums
Gm7 Gm7/C D9 Am7 D9 E♭9 D♭9 D9 Gm7 B♭m7 E♭9 Fmaj7 A7 D7 E♭7 D7
25 26 27 28 29 30 31 32

TO CODA
37
ALTO 1
ALTO 2
TENOR 1
TENOR 2
BARI.
TPT. 1
TPT. 2
TPT. 3
TPT. 4
(TRUMPET)
TBN. 1
TBN. 2
TBN. 3
TBN. 4
GTR.
PNO.
BASS
DRUMS
Gm7
G7 B7 C7
F6 B7(#9)
B♭m7 Cm7 D♭maj7 Em7/A
A♭maj7
Cm7 Bm7
B♭m7
B♭m7 Bdim
FILL
2
33
34
35
36
37
38
39
40

ALTO 1
ALTO 2
TENOR 1
TENOR 2
BARI.
TPT. 1
TPT. 2
TPT. 3
TPT. 4
TBN. 1
TBN. 2
TBN. 3
TBN. 4
GTR.
PNO.
BASS
DRUMS
45
SOLO AD LIB.
FILL
(FLUGEL SOLO)

53
Alto 1
Alto 2
Tenor 1
Tenor 2
Bari.
Tpt. 1
Tpt. 2
Tpt. 3
Tpt. 4
Tbn. 1
Tbn. 2
Tbn. 3
Tbn. 4
Gtr.
Pno.
Bass
Drums
N.V.
End Solo
Cm7 F7 Dm7 C#m7 Cm7 F#m7 B7
B♭m7 E♭7 Cm7 Bm7 B♭m7 Em7 A7 A♭maj7 Cm7 Bm7 B♭m7 B♭m7 Bdim
49
50
51
52
53
54
55
56

Solo Ad Lib.
61
Alto 1
Alto 2
Tenor 1
Tenor 2
Bari.
Tpt. 1
Tpt. 2
Tpt. 3
(To Flugel)
Tpt. 4
Tbn. 1
Tbn. 2
Tbn. 3
Tbn. 4
Gtr.
Pno.
Bass
Drums
Fill
(Alto Solo)
57
58
59
60
61
62
63
64

Alto 1
Alto 2
Tenor 1
Tenor 2
Bari.
Tpt. 1
Tpt. 2
Tpt. 3
Tpt. 4
Tbn. 1
Tbn. 2
Tbn. 3
Tbn. 4
Gtr.
Pno.
Bass
Drums
Gm7
G9
C9
F
Dm7
G7
Cm7
F7
B♭m7
E♭9
69
End Solo
D.S. 𝄋 al Coda
N.V.
Flugel
B♭m7
B♭9
E♭9
E♭+7
A♭
Fm7
B♭7
E♭m7
A♭7
D♭m7
G♭9
Fmaj7
F6
Am7
A♭m7
Gm7
Gm7/C
65
66
67
68
69
70
71
72

Coda
Alto 1
Alto 2
Tenor 1
Tenor 2
Bari.
Tpt. 1
Tpt. 2
Tpt. 3
Tpt. 4
Tbn. 1
Tbn. 2
Tbn. 3
Tbn. 4
Gtr.
F
B7(#9)
B♭m7
Am7
Gm7
Fmaj7
E♭maj7
Gm7/C
Pno.
Bass
Drums
73
74
75
76
77

JEEPERS CREEPERS

Words by JOHNNY MERCER
Music by HARRY WARREN
Arranged by GEORGE ROUMANIS

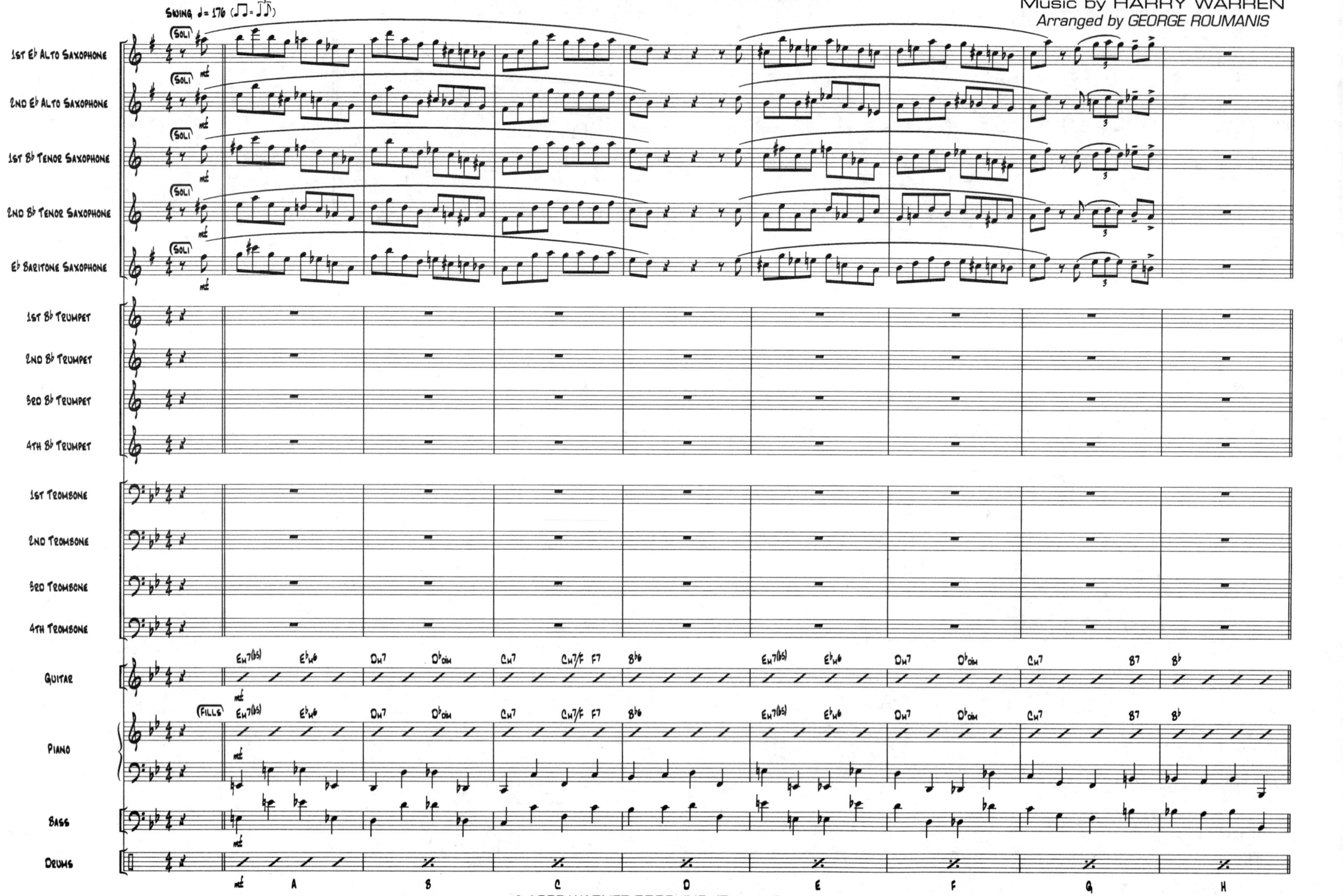

Tacet 1st X
1.)
Play
Plunger
ml-mt
Alto 1
Alto 2
Tenor 1
Tenor 2
Bari.
Tpt. 1
Tpt. 2
Tpt. 3
Tpt. 4
Tbn. 1
Tbn. 2
Tbn. 3
Tbn. 4
Gtr.
Pno.
Bass
Drums
Em7(b5) Ebm6 Dm7 Dbdim Cm7 Cm7/F F7 Bb6 Em7(b5) Ebm6 Dm7 Dbdim Cm7 B7 Bb
Fill
1 2 3 4 5 6 7 8

2.)
11
Alto 1
Alto 2
Tenor 1
Tenor 2
Bari.
Tpt. 1
Tpt. 2
Tpt. 3
Tpt. 4
Tbn. 1
Tbn. 2
Tbn. 3
Tbn. 4
Gtr.
Pno.
Bass
Drums
Open
Open
Fill
Fill
Cm7 B7 B♭ Fm7 B♭9 E♭maj7 C7(♭9) Fm7 B♭9 E♭maj7 E♭6 Gm7 C9 Fmaj7 D7(♭9)
9
10
11
12
13
14
15
16

Alto 1
Alto 2
Tenor 1
Tenor 2
Bari.
Tpt. 1
Tpt. 2
Tpt. 3
Tpt. 4
Tbn. 1
Tbn. 2
Tbn. 3
Tbn. 4
Gtr.
Pno.
Bass
Drums
Plunger
Plunger
Gm7
C9
Fmaj7
Gb7
F9
Em7(b5)
Ebm6
Dm7
Dbdim
Cm7
Cm7/F
F7
Bb6
Em7(b5)
Ebm6
17
18
19
20
21
22
23

29
ALTO 1
ALTO 2
TENOR 1
TENOR 2
BARI.
TPT. 1
TPT. 2
TPT. 3
TPT. 4
TBN. 1
TBN. 2
TBN. 3
TBN. 4
GTR.
PNO.
BASS
DRUMS
LEAD
LEAD
DM7(b5) G7(b9) CM7 F7 Ab9 G9 CM7 B7 Bb CM7 EbM7(b5) DM7 Bdim
DM7(b5) G7(b9) CM7 F7 Ab9 G9 CM7 B7 Bb CM7 EbM7(b5) DM7 Bdim
24
25
26
27
28
29
30

1.)
2.)
ALTO 1
ALTO 2
TENOR 1
TENOR 2
BARI.
TPT. 1
TPT. 2
TPT. 3
TPT. 4
TBN. 1
TBN. 2
TBN. 3
TBN. 4
GTR.
PNO.
BASS
DRUMS
SOLO 1ST TIME
SOLO 2ND TIME
END SOLO
END SOLO
31
32
33
34
35
36
37
38

39
Alto 1
Alto 2
Tenor 1
Solo Gm7 C7 Fmaj7 D7 Gm7 C7 Fmaj7 F6 Am7 D7 Gmaj7 E7(#9) Am7 D7 Dm7 G7
Tenor 2
Bari.
Tpt. 1
Tpt. 2
Tpt. 3
Tpt. 4
Tbn. 1
Tbn. 2
Tbn. 3
Tbn. 4
Gtr.
Fm9 Bb9 Ebmaj7 C7(#9) Fm7 Bb9 Ebmaj7 Eb6 Gm7 C9 Fmaj7 D7(#9) Gm7 C7 Cm7 F7
Pno.
Fm9 Bb9 Ebmaj7 C7(#9) Fm7 Bb9 Ebmaj7 Eb6 Gm7 C9 Fmaj7 D7(#9) Gm7 C7 Cm7 F7
Bass
Fm9 Bb9 Ebmaj7 C7(#9) Fm7 Bb9 Ebmaj7 Eb6 Gm7 C9 Fmaj7 D7(#9) Gm7 C7 Cm7 F7
Drums
39 40 41 42 43 44 45 46

Alto 1
Alto 2
Tenor 1
Tenor 2
Bari.
Tpt. 1
Tpt. 2
Tpt. 3
Tpt. 4
Tbn. 1
Tbn. 2
Tbn. 3
Tbn. 4
Gtr.
Pno.
Bass
Drums
End Solo
Solo
End Solo
47
48
49
50
51
52
53
54

55
1.)
2.)
Alto 1
Alto 2
Tenor 1
Tenor 2
Bari.
Tpt. 1
Tpt. 2
Tpt. 3
Tpt. 4
Tbn. 1
Tbn. 2
Tbn. 3
Tbn. 4
Gtr.
Pno.
Bass
Drums
mf
Solo Both Times
Fmaj7 Fm7
Em7 E♭dim
Dm7 D♭9
C
C End Solo
Em7(♭5) E♭m6
Dm7 D♭dim
Cm7 F7
B♭6 Fm7 B♭7 E7
E♭maj7 E♭m7
Dm7 D♭m7
Cm7 B9
B♭
B♭
55
56
57
58
59
60
61
62
63

64
Alto 1
Alto 2
Tenor 1
Tenor 2
Bari.
Solo Gm7 C7 Fmaj7 D7(#9) Gm7 C7 Fmaj7 F6 Am7 D7 Gmaj7 E7(#9) Am7 D7 G7 End Solo
Tpt. 1
Tpt. 2
Tpt. 3
Tpt. 4
Tbn. 1
Tbn. 2
Tbn. 3
Tbn. 4
Gtr.
Fm7 B♭9 E♭maj7 C7(#9) Fm7 B♭9 E♭maj7 E♭6 Gm7 C7 Fmaj7 D7(#9) Gm7 C7 F9
Pno.
8vb
Bass
Drums
64
65
66
67
68
69
70
71

Alto 1
Alto 2
Tenor 1
Tenor 2
Bari.
Tpt. 1
Tpt. 2
Tpt. 3
Tpt. 4
Tbn. 1
Tbn. 2
Tbn. 3
Tbn. 4
Gtr.
Pno.
Bass
Drums
Em7(b5) Ebм6 Dm7 Dbdim Cm7 F7 Bbм6 Fm7 Bb7 E7 Ebmaj7 Ebм6 Dm7 Dbdim Cm7 Abmaj7 Bmaj7 Bb6
Bb6 - Basie
(8vb)
72
73
74
75
76
77
78
79

80
Alto 1
Alto 2
Tenor 1
Tenor 2
Bari.
(Plunger)
Tpt. 1
Tpt. 2
Tpt. 3
Tpt. 4
(Plunger)
Tbn. 1
Tbn. 2
Tbn. 3
Tbn. 4
Gtr.
Pno.
Bass
Drums
80
81
82
83
84
85
86
87

Alto 1
Alto 2
Tenor 1
Tenor 2
Bari.
Tpt. 1
Tpt. 2
Tpt. 3
Tpt. 4
Tbn. 1
Tbn. 2
Tbn. 3
Tbn. 4
Gtr.
Pno.
Bass
Drums
Em7(b5) Ebm6 Dm7 Dbdim Cm7 Cm7/F F7 Bb6 Em7(b5) Ebm6 Dm7(b5) G7(b9) Cm7 F7 Ab9 G9
88 89 90 91 92 93 94 95

98
Alto 1
Alto 2
Tenor 1
Tenor 2
Bari.
Tpt. 1
Tpt. 2
Tpt. 3
Tpt. 4
Tbn. 1
Tbn. 2
Tbn. 3
Tbn. 4
Gtr.
Pno.
Bass
Drums
Solo
F7
B♭7
E♭7
End Solo
Solo
E♭7
Open
Open
Cm7
B7
B♭
Fm7
B♭9
E♭9
Cm7
B7
8vb
8vb
8vb
Cook behind Tenor Solo
96
97
98
99
100
101
102

ALTO 1
ALTO 2
TENOR 1
TENOR 2
BARI.
TPT. 1
TPT. 2
TPT. 3
TPT. 4
TBN. 1
TBN. 2
TBN. 3
TBN. 4
GTR.
PNO.
BASS
DRUMS
SOLI
A♭7
END SOLO
8VB
FILL
103
104
105
106
107
108
109

AT LAST

Words by MACK GORDON
Music by HARRY WARREN
Arranged by GEORGE ROUMANIS

1.)
2.)
SOLO
ALTO 1
ALTO 2
TENOR 1
TENOR 2
BARI.
TPT. 1
TPT. 2
TPT. 3
TPT. 4
TBN. 1
TBN. 2
TBN. 3
TBN. 4
GTR.
PNO.
BASS
DRUMS
B♭M7 E♭7 A♭MA7 G♭M7 B7 B♭M7 E♭7(♯9) A♭6 D9 D♭MA7 E♭7 B♭M7 E♭7(♭9) A♭6 D9 A♭6
8
9
10
11
12
13
14
15

16
Alto 1
Alto 2
Tenor 1
Tenor 2
Bari.
Tpt. 1
Tpt. 2
Tpt. 3
Tpt. 4
Tbn. 1
Tbn. 2
Tbn. 3
Tbn. 4
Gtr.
Pno.
Bass
Drums
SOLO - SING
B♭m7 E♭9 A♭maj7 Dm7(♭5) G7 Dm7(♭5) A♭9 G9 Cm6 Fm7 B♭9 E♭maj7 C7(♯9) Fm7 B♭+7
16 17 18 19 20 21 22

24
Alto 1
Alto 2
Tenor 1
Tenor 2
Bari.
Tpt. 1
Tpt. 2
Tpt. 3
Tpt. 4
Tbn. 1
Tbn. 2
Tbn. 3
Tbn. 4
Gtr.
Pno.
Bass
Drums
23
24
25
26
27
28

ALTO 1
ALTO 2
TENOR 1
TENOR 2
BARI.
SOLO
TPT. 1
TPT. 2
TPT. 3
TPT. 4
SOLO - AD LIB.
GM7 C7 FM7 B♭7 B♭M7/E♭ E♭7
TBN. 1
TBN. 2
TBN. 3
TBN. 4
GTR.
B♭M7 E♭7 A7 A♭6 D7 B♭M7 D♭M7 GM7 C7 FM7 B♭7 B♭M7/E♭ E♭7
PNO.
BASS
DRUMS
BRASS
W/BASS
29
30
31
32
33
34
35

36
ALTO 1
ALTO 2
TENOR 1
TENOR 2
BARI.
TPT. 1
TPT. 2
TPT. 3
TPT. 4
TBN. 1
TBN. 2
TBN. 3
TBN. 4
GTR.
PNO.
BASS
DRUMS
SOLO
ENS.
A♭6 D♭7(♭5) D♭m7 A♭ Bdim B♭m7 E♭+7 E♭7 A♭maj7 D♭7 G♭7 Cm7 F7 B♭m7 E♭7 A♭maj7 G♭m7 B9 B♭m7 E♭7(♭9) A♭6 D9
36 37 38 39 40 41 42

Alto 1
Alto 2
Tenor 1
Tenor 2
Bari.
Tpt. 1
Tpt. 2
Tpt. 3
Tpt. 4
8va
Cmi7
F7(b9)
Bbmi7
As Is
Abmaj7
Ad Lib. A Few
Tbn. 1
Tbn. 2
Tbn. 3
Tbn. 4
Dbmaj7
Dbmi7/Gb
Gb9
Eb9
Gtr.
Pno.
Arco
Bass
Drums
sfp
43
44
45
46
47

SEPTEMBER IN THE RAIN

Words by AL DUBIN
Music by HARRY WARREN
Arranged by GEORGE ROUMANIS

1.)
2.)
Alto 1
Alto 2
Tenor 1
Tenor 2
Bari.
Tpt. 1
Tpt. 2
Tpt. 3
Tpt. 4
Tbn. 1
Tbn. 2
Tbn. 3
Tbn. 4
Gtr.
Pno.
Bass
Drums
D♭9
Fm7/B♭
E♭(no3rd)
G♭9
Fm7
Fm7/B♭
E♭
D♭9
E♭maj7
E♭(no3rd)
8
9
10
11
12
13
14

15
Alto 1
Alto 2
Tenor 1
Tenor 2
Bari.
Tpt. 1
Tpt. 2
Tpt. 3
Tpt. 4
Tbn. 1
Tbn. 2
Tbn. 3
Tbn. 4
Gtr.
SOLO
Pno.
Bass
Drums
15
16
17
18
19
20
21
22

Alto 1
Alto 2
Tenor 1
Tenor 2
Bari.
Tpt. 1
Tpt. 2
Tpt. 3
Tpt. 4
Tbn. 1
Tbn. 2
Tbn. 3
Tbn. 4
Gtr.
Pno.
Bass
Drums
End Solo
E♭(no3rd) E♭maj7 E♭(no3rd) E♭maj7 E♭(no3rd) A♭6 D♭9 Fm7/B♭ E♭6 G♭9 Fm7 E9
mf
23 24 25 26 27 28 29 30

31
(To Alto - FAST!)
(Alto Sax)
(To Trumpet)
Alto 1
Alto 2
Tenor 1
Tenor 2
Bari.
Tpt. 1
Tpt. 2
Tpt. 3
Tpt. 4
Tbn. 1
Tbn. 2
Tbn. 3
Tbn. 4
Gtr.
Pno.
Bass
Drums
31 32 33 34 35 36 37 38

39
Alto 1
Alto 2
Tenor 1
Tenor 2
Bari.
Tpt. 1
Tpt. 2
Tpt. 3
Tpt. 4
Tbn. 1
Tbn. 2
Tbn. 3
Tbn. 4
Gtr.
Pno.
Bass
Drums
E♭maj7 E♭6 E♭9 A♭maj7 A♭6 A♭maj7 A♭6 D♭9 E♭maj7 D♭m7 G♭9 Cm7 F9 B♭m7 E9
39 40 41 42 43 44 45 46

47
Alto 1
Alto 2
Tenor 1
Tenor 2
Bari.
Tpt. 1
Tpt. 2
Tpt. 3
Tpt. 4
Tbn. 1
Tbn. 2
Tbn. 3
Tbn. 4
Gtr.
Pno.
Bass
Drums
Bbm7 Eb9 Bbm7 Eb9
Bbm9 Eb9
Ab6 Abmaj7 Ab6 Abmaj7
Ab6 Abmaj7
Cm7 F9 Cm7 F9
Cm9 F9
Abmaj7 Gm7 Gbm7
Fm7 E9
Solo
Solo
Solo
47
48
49
50
51
52
53
54

55 Play 3x's
1.)
Alto 1
Alto 2
Tenor 1
Tenor 2
Bari.
Tpt. 1
Tpt. 2
Tpt. 3
Tpt. 4
Tacet 1st Time Only
Plunger
Solo - Play 3rd Time Only
Play
Tbn. 1
Tbn. 2
Tbn. 3
Tbn. 4
Gtr.
Pno.
Solo - 1st Time Only
Bass
Drums
Tacet Figures 1st Time Only
55
56
57
58
59
60
61
62

2.)
3.)
Alto 1
Alto 2
Tenor 1
Tenor 2
Bari.
Tpt. 1
Tpt. 2
Tpt. 3
Tpt. 4
Tbn. 1
Tbn. 2
Tbn. 3
Tbn. 4
Gtr.
Pno.
Bass
Drums
Eb6 Gb9 Fm7 Fm7/Bb
Eb6 Db9 Gb9 C7(#9) Bmaj9 Fm7
8va
63
64
65
66
67
68

ALTO 1
ALTO 2
TENOR 1
TENOR 2
BARI.
TPT. 1
TPT. 2
TPT. 3
TPT. 4
PLUNGER
TBN. 1
TBN. 2
TBN. 3
TBN. 4
GTR.
PNO.
SOLO
8va
PED.
BASS
DRUMS
69
70
71
72

SERENADE IN BLUE

Words by MACK GORDON
Music by HARRY WARREN
Arranged by GEORGE ROUMANIS

14
Alto 1
Alto 2
Tenor 1
Tenor 2
Bari.
Plunger
Open
Tpt. 1
Tpt. 2
Tpt. 3
To Flugel
Tpt. 4
Plunger
Open
Tbn. 1
Tbn. 2
Tbn. 3
Tbn. 4
Gtr.
Pno.
Bass
Drums
9
10
11
12
13
14
15

Alto 1
Alto 2
Tenor 1
Tenor 2
Bari.
Solo - Plunger
Tpt. 1
Tpt. 2
Tpt. 3
Tpt. 4
Tbn. 1
Tbn. 2
Tbn. 3
Tbn. 4
Gtr.
Pno.
Bass
Drums
B♭9 E♭+7 Cm7 Bm7 B♭m7 D♭m7 D♭m6 C+7 F7 B♭7 E♭+7 A♭6 D13
16 17 18 19 20 21

22
ALTO 1
ALTO 2
TENOR 1
TENOR 2
BARI.
TPT. 1
TPT. 2
SOLO - "BLUESY"
TPT. 3
TPT. 4
FLUGEL W/TBNS.
TBN. 1
TBN. 2
TBN. 3
TBN. 4
GTR.
PNO.
BASS
DRUMS
D♭6
D♭M6
BMA7
B♭9
E6
FM7
DM7(♭5)
G7
22
23
24
25
26
27

30
Alto 1
Alto 2
Tenor 1
Tenor 2
Bari.
Tpt. 1
Tpt. 2
Tpt. 3
Tpt. 4
To Trumpet
Solo
Tbn. 1
Tbn. 2
Tbn. 3
Tbn. 4
Gtr.
Pno.
Bass
Drums
Cm7
Bm7 B♭m7
E♭7(♯9)
E7(♯9)
E♭7(♯9)
A♭maj7
Gmaj7 A♭maj7 B♭m7
Cm7
F7(♭9)
F+7
B♭9
E♭7(♭9)
Cm7
Bm7
28
29
30
31
32
33

Alto 1
Alto 2
Tenor 1
Tenor 2
Bari.
Tpt. 1
Tpt. 2
Tpt. 3
Tpt. 4
Tbn. 1
Tbn. 2
Tbn. 3
Tbn. 4
Gtr.
Pno.
Bass
Drums
B♭M7
D♭M7
D♭M6
C7
F7
F+7
B♭9
E♭13
E♭+7
A♭6
A♭9(#11)
D9
A♭M7/D♭
D♭9
34
35
36
37
38
39

42 Double Time Feel - Band Soli
Alto 1
Alto 2
Tenor 1
Tenor 2
Bari.
Tpt. 1
Tpt. 2
Tpt. 3
Tpt. 4
Trumpet
Tbn. 1
Tbn. 2
Tbn. 3
Tbn. 4
End Solo
w/Section
Gtr.
Pno.
Bass
Drums
Ens.
C7
F7
B♭7
E♭7
F7(♭9)
F7(♯9)
C7(♭9)
B♭9
E♭+7
Cm7
Bm7
mf
40
41
42
43
44
45

ALTO 1
ALTO 2
TENOR 1
TENOR 2
BARI.
TPT. 1
TPT. 2
TPT. 3
TPT. 4
TBN. 1
TBN. 2
TBN. 3
TBN. 4
SOLO
GTR.
PNO.
BASS
DRUMS
B♭M7 D♭M7 E♭M7 FM7 GM7 GM6 CM7/F F7 B♭7 E♭7 DM7 D♭M7 CM7 BM7 B♭M7 A♭ B♭M DM7(♭5) B♭M7 E♭7
46
47
48
49
50
51

Soli
Push
Mallets
Alto 1
Alto 2
Tenor 1
Tenor 2
Bari.
Tpt. 1
Tpt. 2
Tpt. 3
Tpt. 4
Tbn. 1
Tbn. 2
Tbn. 3
Tbn. 4
Gtr.
Pno.
Bass
Drums
52
53
54
55

I'VE GOT A GAL IN KALAMAZOO

Words by MACK GORDON
Music by HARRY WARREN
Arranged by GEORGE ROUMANIS

13
Alto 1
Alto 2
Tenor 1
Tenor 2
Bari.
(Open Slowly)
Open
Tpt. 1
Tpt. 2
Tpt. 3
Tpt. 4
Tbn. 1
Tbn. 2
Tbn. 3
Tbn. 4
Gtr.
Pno.
Bass
Drums
9
10
11
12
13
14
15
16

23
Alto 1
Alto 2
Tenor 1
Tenor 2
Bari.
Tpt. 1
Tpt. 2
Tpt. 3
Tpt. 4
Tbn. 1
Tbn. 2
Tbn. 3
Tbn. 4
Gtr.
Pno.
Bass
Drums
17
18
19
20
21
22
23
24

31
Alto 1
Alto 2
Tenor 1
Tenor 2
Bari.
Tpt. 1
Tpt. 2
Tpt. 3
Tpt. 4
Tbn. 1
Tbn. 2
Tbn. 3
Tbn. 4
Gtr.
Pno.
Bass
Drums
C7(b9)
F7(b9) Gb7 F7
F7(b9) Gb7 F7
Bb7 Fm7
F7 Bb7
Ebmaj7 A7(#9)
Abmaj7 Dbmaj7 D7
25 26 27 28 29 30 31 32

Alto 1
Alto 2
Tenor 1
Tenor 2
Bari.
Tpt. 1
Tpt. 2
Tpt. 3
Tpt. 4
Tbn. 1
Tbn. 2
Tbn. 3
Tbn. 4
Gtr.
Pno.
Bass
Drums
FILL
33
34
35
36
37
38
39
40

TO CODA
45
ALTO 1
ALTO 2
TENOR 1
TENOR 2
BARI.
PLAY 1ST X ONLY
TPT. 1
TPT. 2
TPT. 3
TPT. 4
PLAY 1ST X ONLY
TBN. 1
TBN. 2
TBN. 3
TBN. 4
GTR.
PNO.
BASS
FILL
DRUMS
41
42
43
44
45
46
47

Alto 1
Alto 2
Tenor 1
Tenor 2
Bari.
Play Both X's
To Plunger
Tpt. 1
Tpt. 2
Tpt. 3
Tpt. 4
Play Both X's
To Plunger
Tbn. 1
Tbn. 2
Tbn. 3
Tbn. 4
Gtr.
Pno.
Bass
Drums
A♭maj7 D7(♭9) E♭ D7(♭9) D♭9 C7(♯9) Fm7 B♭9 E♭6 A7(♯9) A♭maj7 D7(♭9) E♭6
A♭maj7 D7(♭9) E♭ D7(♭9) D♭9 C7(♯9) Fm7 B♭9 E♭6 A7(♯9) A♭maj7 D7(♭9) E♭m7/G♭
48
49
50
51
52
53
54

55
D.S. 𝄋 AL CODA
ALTO 1
ALTO 2
TENOR 1
TENOR 2
BARI.
TPT. 1
TPT. 2
TPT. 3
TPT. 4
TBN. 1
TBN. 2
TBN. 3
TBN. 4
GTR.
PNO.
BASS
DRUMS
SOLO - AD LIB. AROUND MELODY
55
56
57
58
59
60
61
62

Coda
Rit.
Push Triplet
Cut Off - As Conducted
Alto 1
Alto 2
Tenor 1
Tenor 2
Bari.
To Plunger
On Cue
Tpt. 1
Tpt. 2
Tpt. 3
Tpt. 4
Tbn. 1
Tbn. 2
Tbn. 3
Tbn. 4
Gtr.
Pno.
Bass
Drums
Fill
63
64
65
66

WE'RE IN THE MONEY

Words by AL DUBIN
Music by HARRY WARREN
Arranged by GEORGE ROUMANIS

13
Alto 1
Alto 2
Tenor 1
Tenor 2
Bari.
Tpt. 1
Tpt. 2
Tpt. 3
Tpt. 4
Tbn. 1
Tbn. 2
Tbn. 3
Tbn. 4
Gtr.
Pno.
Bass
Drums
sfp
Wah
Plunger
mf
Ab6 Ab9 Db6 Gb9 Ab6 Fm7 Bb7 Eb7 Ab6
Cm Fm7 Ebmaj7 Dm7(b5) G7(b9) G+7 Cm6 G+7
9 10 11 12 13 14 15 16

Alto 1
Alto 2
Tenor 1
Tenor 2
Bari.
Tpt. 1
Tpt. 2
Tpt. 3
Tpt. 4
Tbn. 1
Tbn. 2
Tbn. 3
Tbn. 4
Gtr.
Pno.
Bass
Drums
17
18
19
20
21
22
23
24

Alto 1
Alto 2
Tenor 1
Tenor 2
Bari.
Tpt. 1
Tpt. 2
Tpt. 3
Tpt. 4
Tbn. 1
Tbn. 2
Tbn. 3
Tbn. 4
Gtr.
Pno.
Bass
Drums
29
mf
sfp
WAH
A♭6 A♭9 D♭6 G♭9 A♭6 Fm7 B♭7 E♭7 A♭6 B♭m7 E♭7 A♭6 F7(♭9) B♭m7 E♭9 A♭6 F7(♭9) B♭m7 E♭9
2
25
26
27
28
29
30
31
32

1.)
2.)
39
Alto 1
Alto 2
Tenor 1
Tenor 2
Bari.
Tpt. 1
Tpt. 2
Tpt. 3
Tpt. 4
Tbn. 1
Tbn. 2
Tbn. 3
Tbn. 4
Gtr.
Pno.
Bass
Drums
Solo - 1st X Only
Solo - 2nd X Only
End Solo
Solo
Open 2nd X
Open
mf
Ab7
Db6
Gb9
Abmaj7
F7(b9)
Bb9
Eb9
Cm7
Bbm7
G7(b9)
Cm6
Fm7
Ebmaj7
Dm7(b5)
Bb7
Eb
Ebm6
Bbmaj7
C9
F9
Dm7
A7
Dm
Gm7
Fmaj7
Em7(b5)
33
34
35
36
37
38
39
40

47
Alto 1
Alto 2
Tenor 1
Tenor 2
Bari.
Tpt. 1
Tpt. 2
Tpt. 3
Tpt. 4
Tbn. 1
Tbn. 2
Tbn. 3
Tbn. 4
Gtr.
Pno.
Bass
Drums
A+7 Dm A+7 Dm6 Gm7 Fmaj7 Dm6 A♭7 G7 F♯7 F7 End Solo
Solo
B♭ G7(♭9) Cm7 F7
To Plunger
G+7 Cm G+7 Cm6 Fm7 E♭maj7 Cm6 G♭9 F9 E9 E♭9 A♭maj7 F7(♭9) B♭m7 E♭7(♭9)
41 42 43 44 45 46 47 48

Alto 1
Alto 2
Tenor 1
Tenor 2
Bari.
Tpt. 1
Tpt. 2
Tpt. 3
Tpt. 4
Tbn. 1
Tbn. 2
Tbn. 3
Tbn. 4
Gtr.
Pno.
Bass
Drums
55
Plunger
WAH
Open
mf
49
50
51
52
53
54
55
56

1.)
2.)
ALTO 1
ALTO 2
TENOR 1
TENOR 2
BARI.
TPT. 1
TPT. 2
TPT. 3
TPT. 4
TBN. 1
TBN. 2
TBN. 3
TBN. 4
GTR.
PNO.
BASS
DRUMS
FILL
FILL
57
58
59
60
61
62
63
64

65
ALTO 1
ALTO 2
TENOR 1
TENOR 2
BARI.
TPT. 1
TPT. 2
TPT. 3
TPT. 4
TBN. 1
TBN. 2
TBN. 3
TBN. 4
GTR.
PNO.
BASS
DRUMS
mf
CRESC.
Cm6 Fm7 E♭maj7 Dm7(♭5) G9 G7(♭9) Cm6 G+7(♯9) Cm6 Fm7 E♭maj7 Cm6 D♭m7 G♭9 Cm7 F9 Bm7 E7 B♭m7 E♭7
65
66
67
68
69
70
71
72

73
Play 3 Times
Alto 1
Alto 2
Tenor 1
Tenor 2
Bari.
Tpt. 1
Tpt. 2
Tpt. 3
Tpt. 4
Tbn. 1
Tbn. 2
Tbn. 3
Tbn. 4
Gtr.
Pno.
Bass
Drums
To Plunger
Plunger
Wah
A♭6 Adim B♭m7 E♭7 A♭6 Adim B♭m7 E♭7 A♭6 A♭9 D♭6 G♭9 A♭6 Fm7 B♭7 E♭7 A♭ F7/E♭
73 74 75 76 77 78 79 80

1-2.)
3.)
ALTO 1
ALTO 2
TENOR 1
TENOR 2
BARI.
TPT. 1
TPT. 2
TPT. 3
TPT. 4
TBN. 1
TBN. 2
TBN. 3
TBN. 4
GTR.
PNO.
BASS
DRUMS
WAH
OPEN
SOLO FILL
FILL
81
82
83
84
85
86
87
88